alphabet poem: for kids!

emily critchley
michael kindellan
and
alison honey woods

To our children

Agnes

Elena

Greta

Martha

Oliver

Poppy

A

A is a very good point to begin. It is balancy
on both arms and ankles. A little shiny, A aaahs
like amity, love-arrows or poetry ailanthus.*
Under such angles you can hide out also.
Small a's a fresh-picked apple:
that tastes awesome.

*'tree of heaven!' Lee Ann Brown, 'Ailanthus'

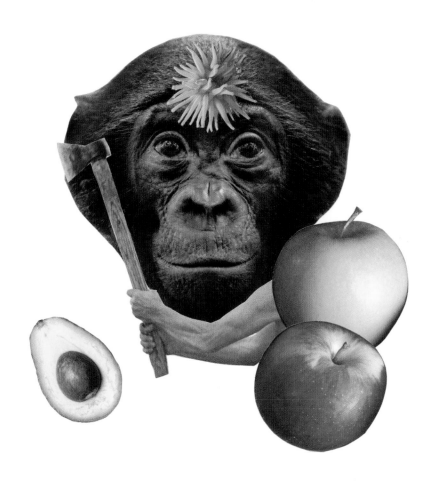

B

But should I mention B for instance, may be the name
the B may have and have to come to use? For baby
or bear or ball it may appear to move across the bumps of wall
with strangeness. Though bumps of strangeness—
and a line—align when 'baa' they call.

C

Coming to catch silent 'c' on the back
of a sock or duck. Afterwards
a cat nap, cuddles: we like the sound of that
even if it's havoc in the clouds
which chase us crazily
while cool we count
them –

D

Dee, dee, Dinkelbrot! Did you knead your dough?!?!

No! no! no! no! no – no – no – no – no!

Dargh! Darn Dinkelbrot! Don't you depress me so.

Oh! oh! oh! oh! oh – oh – oh – oh – oh!

Die! Die! Dinkelbrot! You're dealt a ridgèd blow!

So? so? so? so? so – so – so – so – so?!?!

Dah! Dah! Dinkelbrot! Let your dents all grow!

E

There is an Elena standing in a poem!

And there is an Elena now.

There is also there a here
a something – eek – exciting!

& there is too this peek
-a-boo of eager
-ness, this ebb
and easy flow.

And everything begins with e
while every child deserves
the good earth as they go.

F

Wallace wrote a little ration of effs and dees:
'the bird's fire fangled feathers dangle down',
being merely the final folia that line does foil;
John jotted down 'fee fie foe fum, I smell the blood
na' ENGlish mun'; Will's 'fathom five this father
lies' s'a full fun fiver'unner; in sum: alliteration's
all iteration, of effs or dees or cees, you see,
and hear, and form from lips, flung ear to ear.

G

Gee-whiz my kid,
 the girl my gal's gone
   made and gave
 a *Mädchen* for,
   and we to be
     the ones who give
   and grab you when a-going,
 gone or goofing
     on the ground. An-
   a-gram of great
     we (until recently)
       'geed' *hin und her*
         until *du ganz allein gegangen*
       bist and we, agog,
         went 'go Greta go!'

H

How happy
things like that
which happen in
the stance of baby
(now a little girl)
who's standing amongst
language liking
learning letters
'HELLO ALPHABET!'
we holler at you
counting hi-fives
in our hands
(or under bushels)
while — hooray — we
feed her words
like hungry hippos
heart her hopefully.

I

'I' is a letter
that we very
often see.
'I' is a letter
that means
when I say me.
'I' asks myself
do I know
a different we.
But I am not
a letter no matter
which 'I' be.

J

Jump this jangling toward James-ness!

                      This jamming joyjuice!

      Now we see him

         (now we don't)

in jokey jimjams

                juggling loveliness

  + toothy jitter-gaps

         from pancake jiving.

How he hijinks –

               hits the jackpot

    (tooth-mouse)

          to the jing jing jing jing jing...

          of jocund dawn.

K

for Koto Daisy Atkins

Hey Kindellan,
do you want to kickstart
or should I
this kinaesthetic cut-up
which our cute kids
skip & kiss & swap
or play at kolorscape
as Kotes with me?
Umbrellas keep us
cosy when the rain
kaleidoscopes —
we feel that keenly
on our knuckles, OK so
we put the kettle on & run
for cover...!

L

In lieu of lilies like
loose-let loops long
linked, lithe little
leaps leanly loan
lights to lift, listing
litanies of lively lamps.
Lest lessons levy lies
that lilt the limber limbs
lined up, and link lips
to lids laid with loads,
we loll, lodge, lock,
lead, laugh, lay
and love. You land
last, my lady's labour.

M

for Martha Knutsen

Time mounts most long
to this mid-morning's mean.
A medium, murky Monday,
mime room meshed by mouse's
moves; a mouse's moves
mean maybe mice might
brightly, softly calm many
famous, stormy forms & mend
the days to-morrow. My! As
slim mouths mull, and munch,
and mewl. What mother wouldn't
mind? Amazed by middles,
mirrors, riddles, and other many
minds whose meanings are
mostly mixed up in all the
me-s it finds, in 'I' and 'she'
and 'you'... 'Em, o, Em',
this poem's mighty overdue!

N

Nocturne

And now & now & now & now & now
what goes, what comes, what goes, what comes, what goes
is it, is that, is it, is what is naught
below, above, below, above, below
the new, the now, the nigh, the nightly now
it is, is not, it is, is what is not
the this from that, the this from what is what
and now & now & now & now & now
the nigh is night, the night is nicely nigh
is not, it is, is not, is nightly nigh
the knot of naught is night
and night is now.

O

Baby
is mouthing
O o o o s over you
blowing bubbles, opal,
on octopus. And something
is shaped like an O (especially *no!*),
while something is old as the ocean,
amorous, so. And I obviously
owe all that to you: my
only, my
oh.

P

Poems! The problem
with poetry! Explain,
poets! Perfectly content!
And as for a poetics!
Our art abandons us...

Q

for Meredith Gordon

Quick quick quick
says the duck
Quack quack quack
as they smack
Qua qua qua
squawk the birds
Queria queria queria
who could be merrier?

R

A tiger goes
grrrr
& girls go
grrrr &
tigers go
grrrr
& a girl
goes grrrr
& tigers &
girls go grrrr
grrrr grrrr...

S

To sing quickly over the sensations, to sow
movement carried forward & changing
and sometimes sorrowed. Then changed in shape
or softly, withdrawn in favour of something else's
place, like casting away mountains and up-
setting the sea: sudden. Over a season
to start, to stir all the emotions very varied
after all of this slow time. To send
a letter, to turn over a stress,
open to lean and wasted certainty, siphoned
in seeing slightly, inviting a friend to shift
the sadness of sore. To say by dispatch,
to show to sigh, resigning the service,
and the boat see-sawing, slowed
with a leaf, spinning. And to come
back, hand over hand over hand, safely
on time some time, to ask to move closer,
and not to alter a sign for once sure.

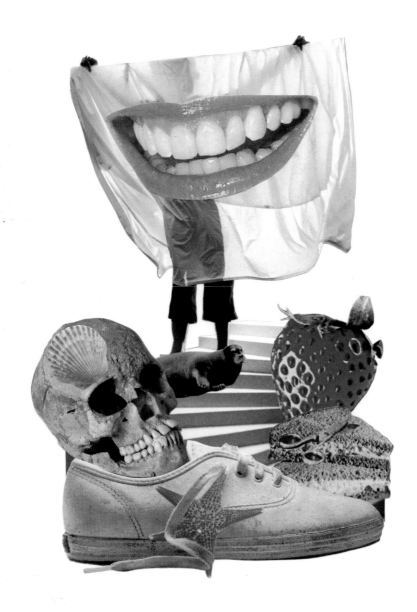

T

It's time for t, t'isn't it?
T'is true! Tee, tea, tee-hee
hee. T is for tooth and t
is for that, t is for things
which tangle and tap.
Tea for teatime and
toast and for treacle,
tee means to tip-toe
and trip means to topple.
The tie that I tie when I
tie a tight knot is tantamount,
just about, more-or-less
it. The tees that we wear
are shaped like we are,
the trees that we climb
are too tall to tell. Those
trades and those tricks we're
taught well to turn, turn
out to be traces of stuff
others learn. Today traffic
and trains and trams
trundle by, 'Straßenbahn,
Straßenbahn' goes your
little cry. Thence home
and to tea, there's time for
a bath. Though tiny one's
tired the tunes tinkle on:
'twinkle, twinkle...'

U

U is a difficult
it is utterly um
under uh uncertainty
may be a place-
holder, but also undeniably
the 21st letter
in a new era (shorthand)
oh speech counterpart of orthographic *u*
as grade-rating: unsatisfactory
but how could that be!
U is unbelievably unanimously
unconditionally unequivocally
uniquely & unerringly
undividable
from me.

V

Venus, bright star,
second from the sun;
vacation, not far,
but very, super fun;
via, a way, on par
with how you run;
ein Vogel, sogar,
fliegt genau herum;
things vu, déjà, are
not already come.

Wherefore the wind, it is a wistful wind.
It woooos in woods and wonderfully...
It can be very wanting / wild round trees
or whet against the waves, whereby it waits
& wears, so warily, then whips! like wings
against a way. Woooshes to withdrawing
workaday. Or wiles while weak, then wows
& wins withal whatever in the weathered world
that wills or leaves its will: now whimsily,
now waningly, but never to withdraw
without it wishing, well now, wishing
all things well.

X

```
X O X
O X X
O X O
```

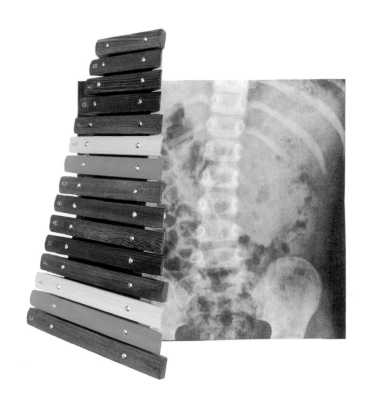

Y

Yee-haw and yeah. Yams're
yum, yes? Your yellow yesses
yelp you yonder. Y'all yaks
yammer, yank, yap, yark.
Your yarns yarning. Yo!
Yawns yall, yays yamp.
Years yearn, yield yeas
n' yas. Yip! Yiz! Yo-yos-yo-yoed,
yodelers yodeled, yoghurt's
yolk yikes. You-hoo's yore's
young yet, youthful Yow!

Z

Zip zip zip:
baby grows up quick!
Sein und zeit:
baby's all alright
Zoom zing zeal:
baby's full of squeal
Sie so zäh:
baby's
baby's
all the way from zzzzz
to aaah.

Index of Poems

About the Authors

Emily Critchley is the author of twelve poetry collections, including *Arrangements* (Shearsman, 2018) and *Ten Thousand Things* (Boiler House Press, 2017). She is Senior Lecturer in English and Creative Writing at the University of Greenwich and lives in London with her daughter. Her most recent manuscript, *Home*, is forthcoming with Prototype.

Alison Honey Woods is a visual artist, photographer and filmmaker. She lives in Toronto with her husband Chris, children Oliver and Poppy, and their dog, Wolfy.

Michael Kindellan is a Canadian-born poet and scholar. He lives in Berlin with partner Julia and their daughters Greta and Agnes.

Acknowledgements

We wish to thank Jess Chandler & all at Prototype for bringing our book into the world. Also, thanks to partners, fellow poets & everyone who makes our writing context a happy one.

About Prototype

poetry / prose / interdisciplinary projects / anthologies

Creating new possibilities in the publishing of fiction and poetry through a flexible, interdisciplinary approach and the production of unique and beautiful books.

Prototype is an independent publisher working across genres and disciplines, committed to discovering and sharing work that exists outside the mainstream.

Each publication is unique in its form and presentation, and the aesthetic of each object is considered critical to its production.

Prototype strives to increase audiences for experimental writing, as the home for writers and artists whose work requires a creative vision not offered by mainstream literary publishers.

In its current, evolving form, Prototype consists of 4 strands of publications: (type 1 // poetry) / (type 2 // prose) / (type 3 // interdisciplinary projects) / (type 4 // anthologies).

( ) (   )

prototype publishing

71 oriel road

london e9 5sg

uk

Design by Theo Inglis

Typeset in Sassoon Infant and
Plantin Infant

Printed in the UK by
TJ International

A CIP record for this book is
available from the British Library

ISBN: 978-1-9160520-3-1

( )   (   )

p   prototype

(type 3 // interdisciplinary projects)

www.prototypepublishing.co.uk
@prototypepubs